W9-CAG-551

Inch by Inch

by Leo Lionni

SCHOLASTIC INC. New York Toronto London Auckland Sydney

ISBN 0-590-47991-1

 Published by Scholastic
Inc., 555 Broadway, New York, NY 10012, by arrangement with Astor Honor/
Division of Beauty Fashion.

58 57 56 55 54 17 18 19 20 21/0

Printed in the U.S.A. 08

First Scholastic printing, March 1994

One day a hungry robin saw an inchworm, green as an emerald,
sitting on a twig. He was about to gobble him up.

"Don't eat me. I am an inchworm. I am useful.
I measure things."
"Is that so!" said the robin. "Then measure my tail!"

"That's easy," said the inchworm.
"One, two, three, four, five inches."

“Just think,” said the robin, “my tail is five inches long!”
And with the inchworm, he flew to where other birds needed to be measured.

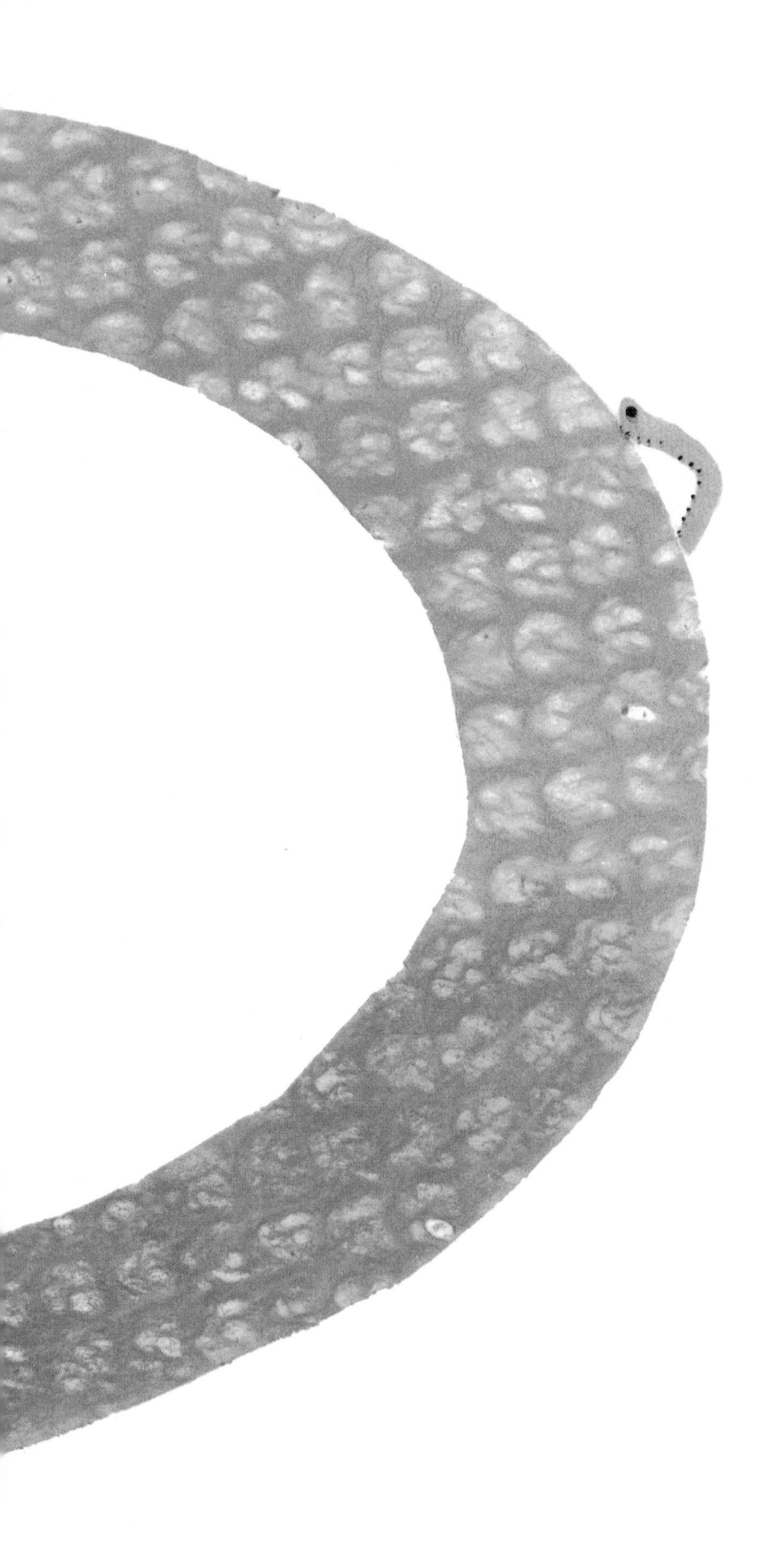

The inchworm measured the neck of the flamingo.

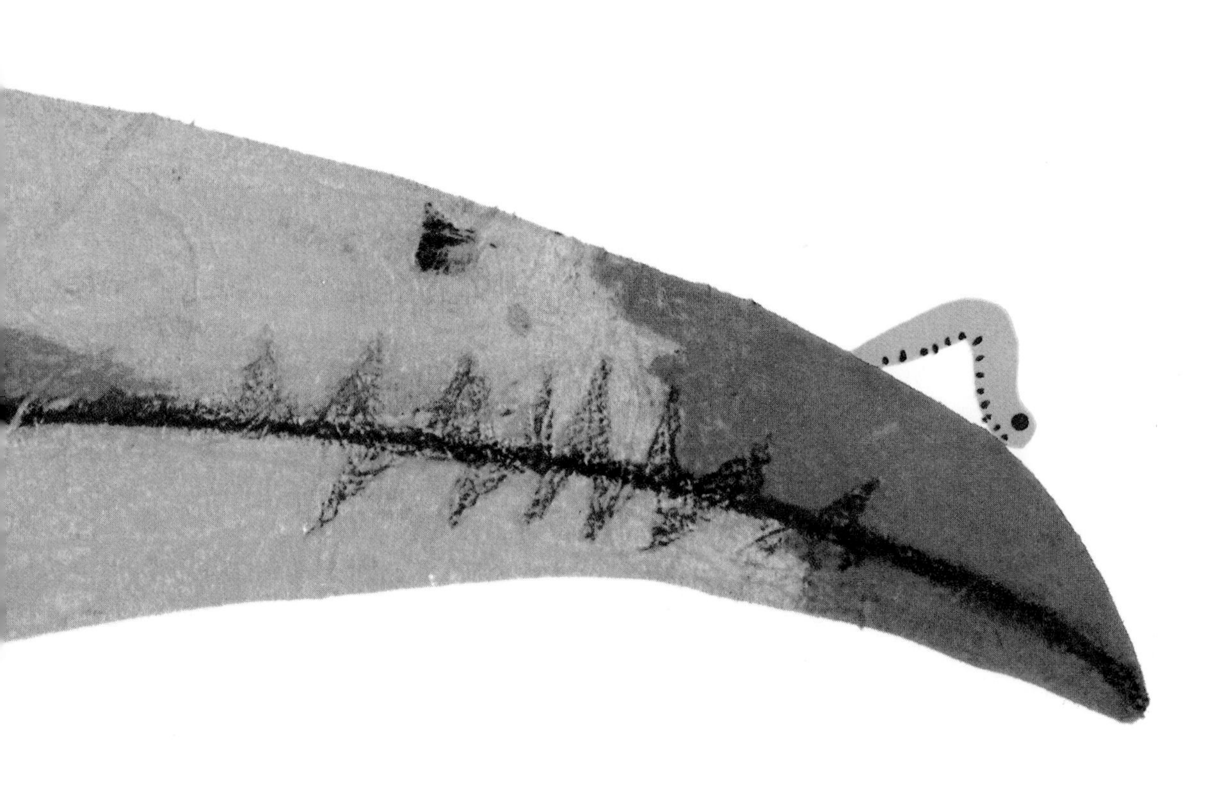

He measured the toucan's beak...

the legs of the heron...

the tail of the pheasant...

and the whole hummingbird.

One morning, the nightingale met the inchworm.
"Measure my song," said the nightingale.
"But how can I do that?" said the inchworm. "I measure things, not songs.
"Measure my song or I'll eat you for breakfast," said the nightingale.
Then the inchworm had an idea.

"I'll try," he said, "go ahead and sing."

The nightingale sang and the inchworm measured away.

He measured and measured...

Inch by Inch...

until he inched out of sight.